THE RACONTEURS. BROKEN BOY SOLDIERS

THE RACONTEURS. BROKEN BOY SOLDIERS

Published by
Wise Publications
14-15 Berners Street, London, W1T 3LJ, UK.

Exclusive distributors:
Music Sales Limited
Distribution Centre, Newmarket Road,
Bury St Edmunds, Suffolk, IP33 3YB, UK.

Music Sales Pty Limited
120 Rothschild Avenue, Rosebery,
NSW 2018, Australia.

Order No. AM986304
ISBN 1-84609-656-1
This book © Copyright 2006 Wise Publications,
a division of Music Sales Limited.

Edited by David Weston.
Music processed by Paul Ewers Music Design.

Printed in the EU.

www.musicsales.com

Remember a time
when all was not fine
and up from the dingy sewers
came four lousy thieves
who flourished like trees
behold The Raconteurs...

WISE PUBLICATIONS
PART OF THE MUSIC SALES GROUP
London / New York / Paris / Sydney / Copenhagen / Berlin / Madrid / Tokyo

GUITAR TABLATURE EXPLAINED
GUITAR MUSIC CAN BE NOTATED IN THREE DIFFERENT WAYS: ON A MUSICAL STAVE, IN TABLATURE, AND IN RHYTHM SLASHES

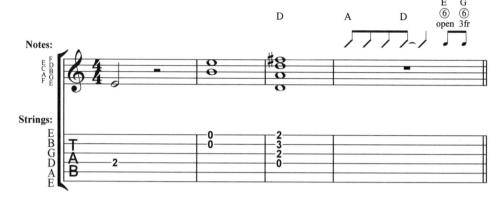

RHYTHM SLASHES: are written above the stave. Strum chords in the rhythm indicated. Round noteheads indicate single notes.

THE MUSICAL STAVE: shows pitches and rhythms and is divided by lines into bars. Pitches are named after the first seven letters of the alphabet.

TABLATURE: graphically represents the guitar fingerboard. Each horizontal line represents a string, and each number represents a fret.

DEFINITIONS FOR SPECIAL GUITAR NOTATION

SEMI-TONE BEND: Strike the note and bend up a semi-tone (½ step).

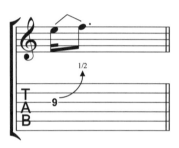

WHOLE-TONE BEND: Strike the note and bend up a whole-tone (full step).

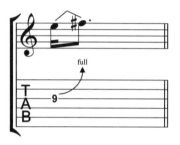

GRACE NOTE BEND: Strike the note and bend as indicated. Play the first note as quickly as possible.

QUARTER-TONE BEND: Strike the note and bend up a ¼ step

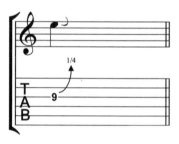

BEND & RELEASE: Strike the note and bend up as indicated, then release back to the original note.

COMPOUND BEND & RELEASE: Strike the note and bend up and down in the rhythm indicated.

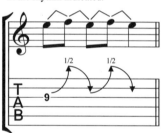

PRE-BEND: Bend the note as indicated, then strike it.

PRE-BEND & RELEASE: Bend the note as indicated. Strike it and release the note back to the original pitch.

HAMMER-ON: Strike the first note with one finger, then sound the second note (on the same string) with another finger by fretting it without picking.

PULL-OFF: Place both fingers on the note to be sounded, strike the first note and without picking, pull the finger off to sound the second note.

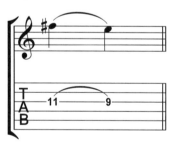

LEGATO SLIDE (GLISS): Strike the first note and then slide the same fret-hand finger up or down to the second note. The second note is not struck.

MUFFLED STRINGS: A percussive sound is produced by laying the first hand across the string(s) without depressing, and striking them with the pick hand.

NATURAL HARMONIC: Strike the note while the fret-hand lightly touches the string directly over the fret indicated.

PICK SCRAPE: The edge of the pick is rubbed down (or up) the string, producing a scratchy sound.

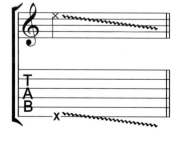

PALM MUTING: The note is partially muted by the pick hand lightly touching the string(s) just before the bridge.

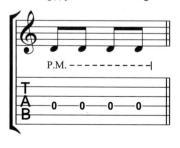

SHIFT SLIDE (GLISS & RESTRIKE): Same as legato slide, except the second note is struck.

SLAP HARMONIC: The note is fretted normally and a harmonic is produced by 'slapping' the fret indicated in brackets (which will be twelve frets higher than the fretted note.)

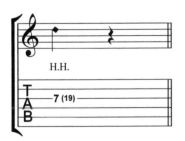

TAPPING: Hammer ('tap') the fret indicated with the pick-hand index or middle finger and pull-off to the note fretted by the fret hand.

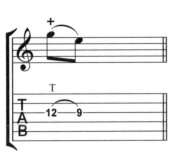

PINCH HARMONIC: The note is fretted normally and a harmonic is produced by adding the edge of the thumb or the tip of the index finger of the pick hand to the normal pick attack.

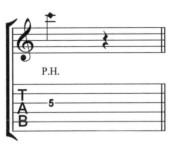

HARP HARMONIC: The note is fretted normally and a harmonic is produced by gently resting the pick hand's index finger directly above the indicated fret (in brackets) while plucking the appropriate string.

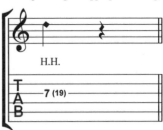

TRILL: Very rapidly alternate between the notes indicated by continuously hammering-on and pulling-off.

RAKE: Drag the pick across the strings with a single motion.

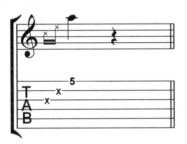

TREMOLO PICKING: The note is picked as rapidly and continuously as possible.

ARPEGGIATE: Play the notes of the chord indicated by quickly rolling them from bottom to top.

SWEEP PICKING: Rhythmic downstroke and/or upstroke motion across the strings.

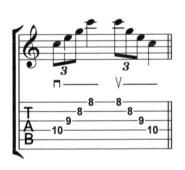

VIBRATO DIVE BAR AND RETURN: The pitch of the note or chord is dropped a specific number of steps (in rhythm) then returned to the original pitch.

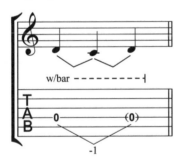

VIBRATO BAR SCOOP: Depress the bar just before striking the note, then quickly release the bar.

VIBRATO BAR DIP: Strike the note and then immediately drop a specific number of steps, then release back to the original pitch.

ADDITIONAL MUSICAL DEFINITIONS

 (accent)   Accentuate note (play it louder)

D.S. al Coda   Go back to the sign (𝄋), then play until the bar marked *To Coda* ⊕ then skip to the section marked ⊕ *Coda*

 (accent)   Accentuate note with greater intensity

D.C. al Fine   Go back to the beginning of the song and play until the bar marked *Fine.*

 (staccato)   Shorten time value of note

tacet   Instrument is silent (drops out).

⊓   Downstroke

∨   Upstroke

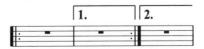   Repeat bars between signs

NOTE: Tablature numbers in brackets mean:
1. The note is sustained, but a new articulation (such as hammer-on or slide) begins
2. A note may be fretted but not necessarily played.

When a repeat section has different endings, play the first ending only the first time and the second ending only the second time.

7

STEADY, AS SHE GOES

WORDS & MUSIC BY
JACK WHITE & BRENDAN BENSON

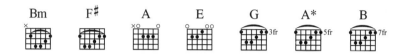

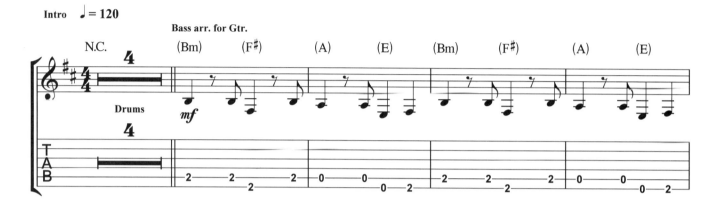

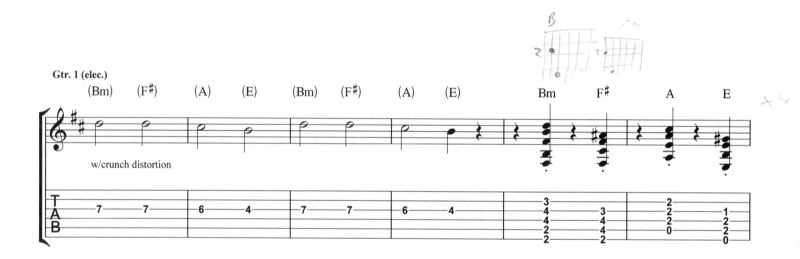

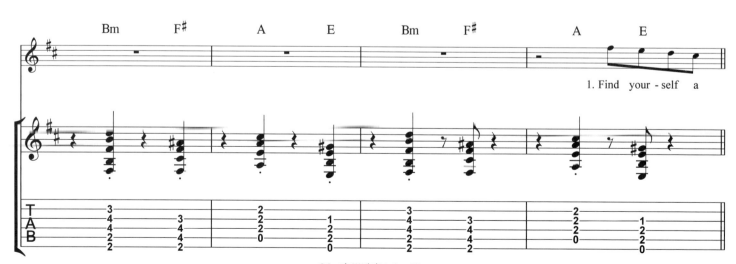

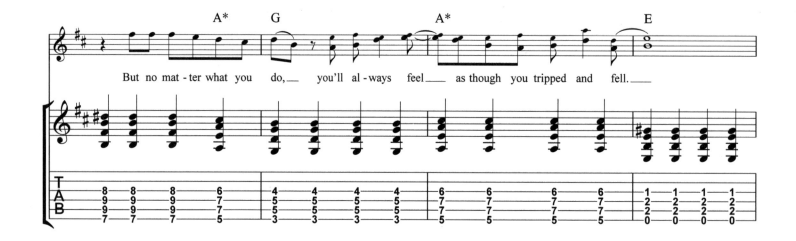

But no mat - ter what you do,___ you'll al -ways feel___ as though you tripped and fell.___

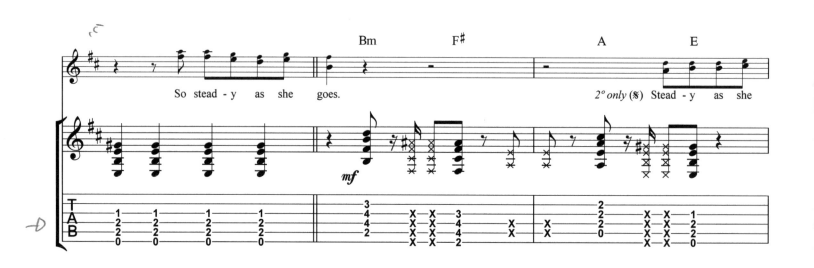

So stead - y as she goes.

2° only (𝄋) Stead - y as she

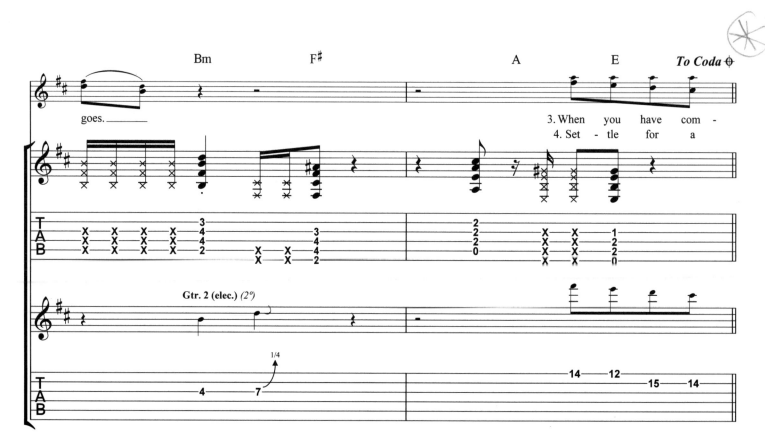

goes.___

3. When you have com -
4. Set - tle for a

Gtr. 2 (elec.) *(2°)*

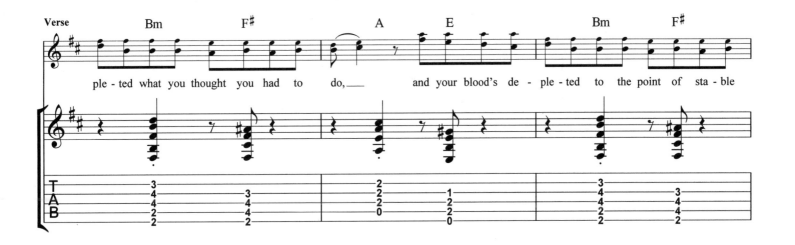

Verse Bm F# A E Bm F#

ple - ted what you thought you had to do, ___ and your blood's de - ple - ted to the point of sta - ble

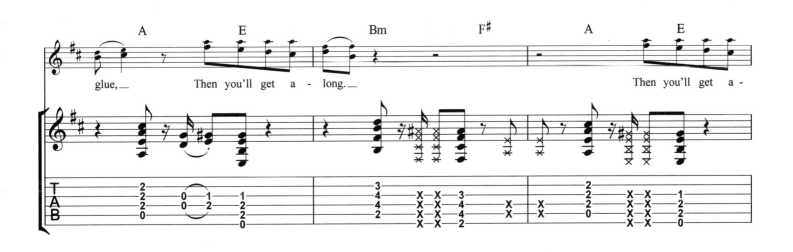

A E Bm F# A E

glue, ___ Then you'll get a - long. ___ Then you'll get a -

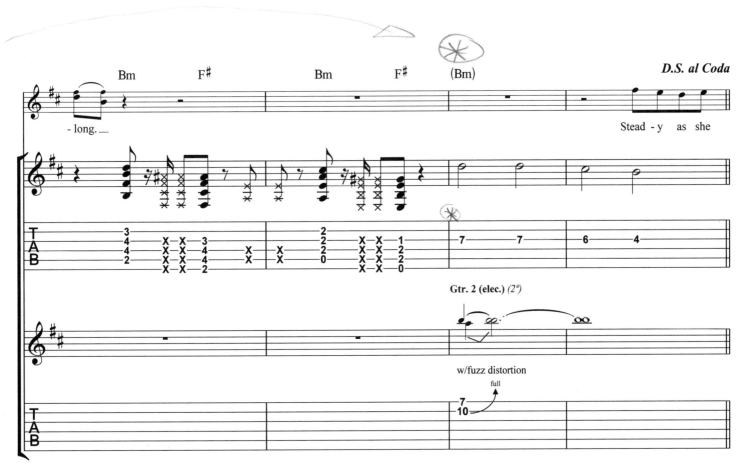

Bm F# Bm F# (Bm) *D.S. al Coda*

- long. ___ Stead - y as she

Gtr. 2 (elec.) *(2°)*

w/fuzz distortion

full

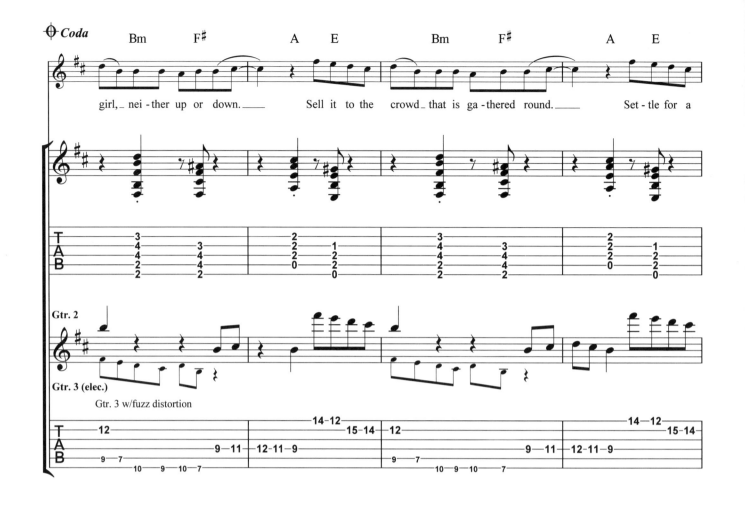

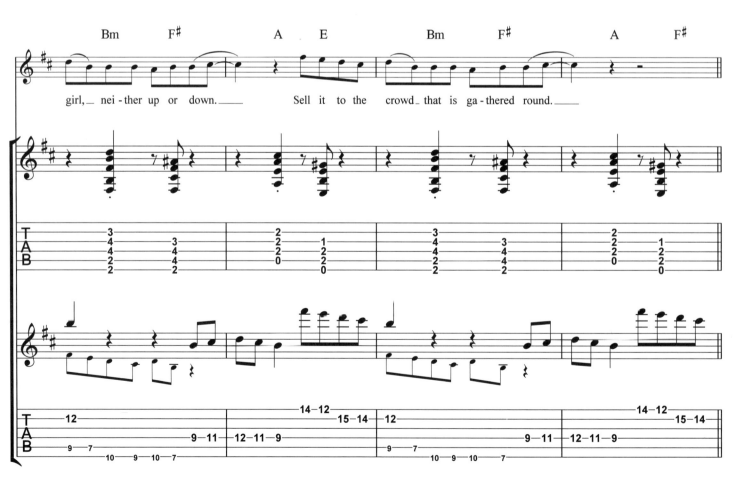

Interlude

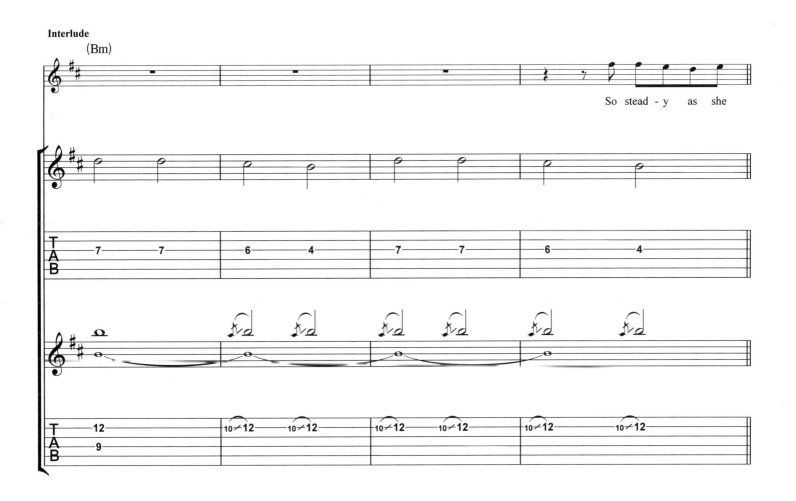

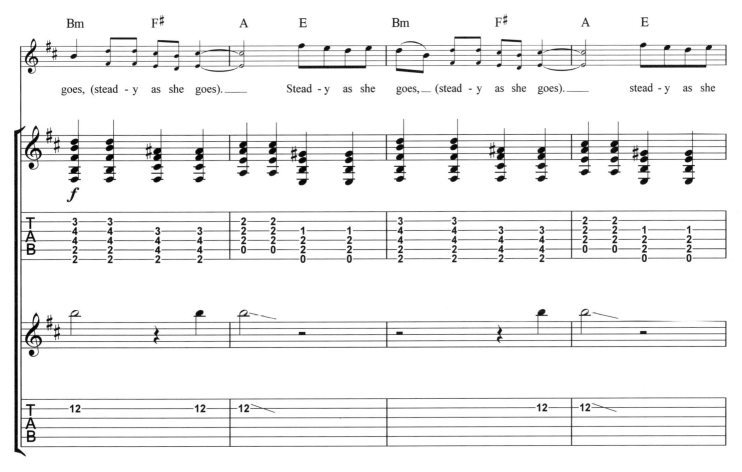

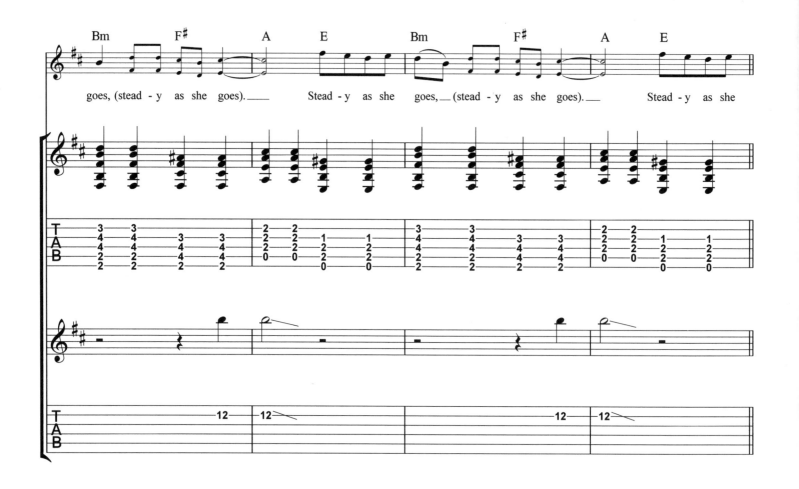

goes, (stead - y as she goes). ___ Stead - y as she goes, (stead - y as she goes). ___ Stead - y as she

Outro

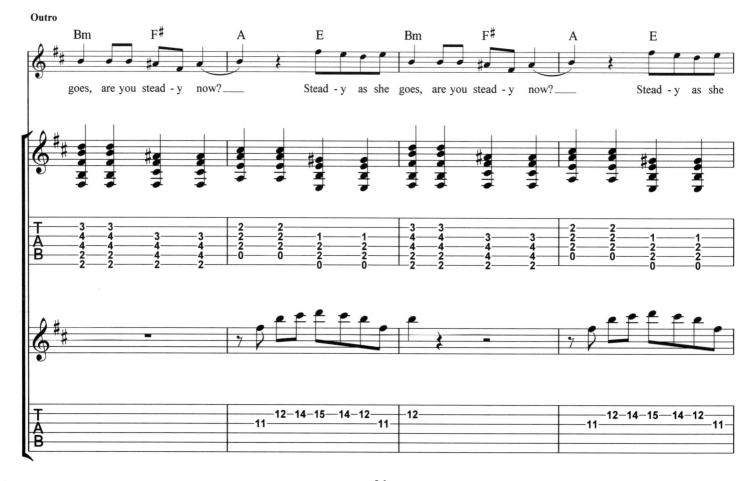

goes, are you stead - y now? ___ Stead - y as she goes, are you stead - y now? ___ Stead - y as she

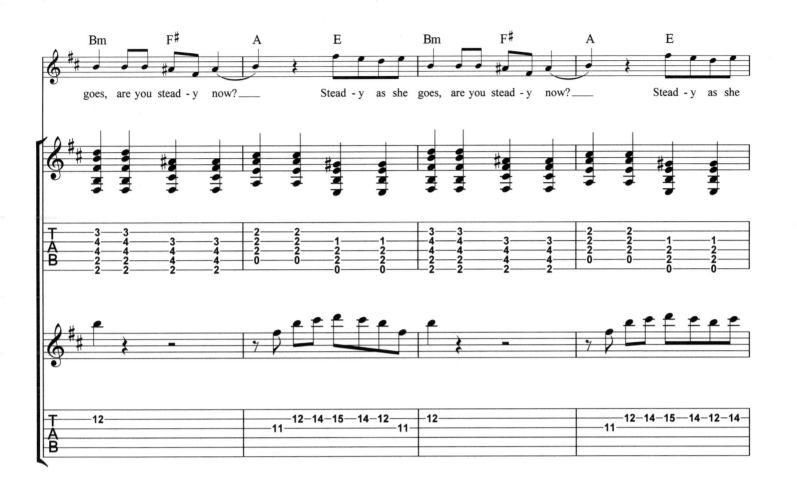

goes, are you stead-y now?____ Stead-y as she goes, are you stead-y now?____ Stead-y as she

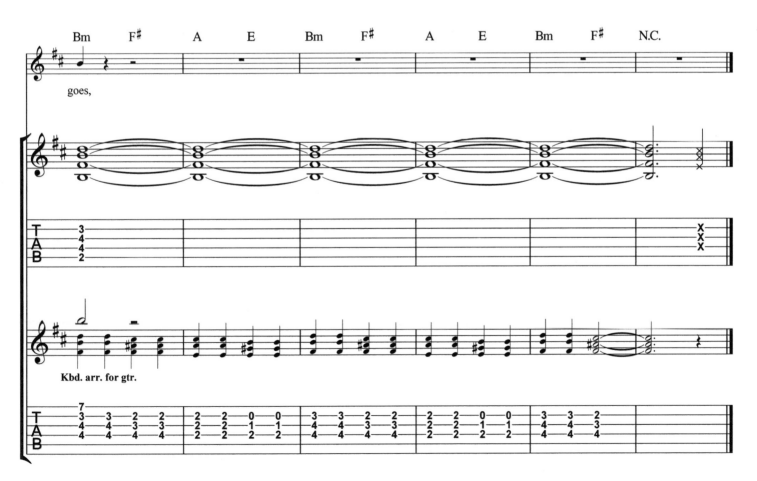

goes,

Kbd. arr. for gtr.

HANDS

WORDS & MUSIC BY
JACK WHITE & BRENDAN BENSON

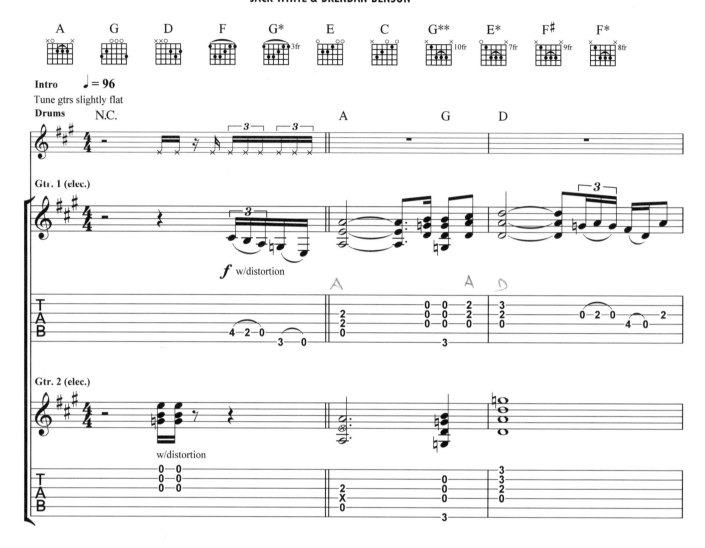

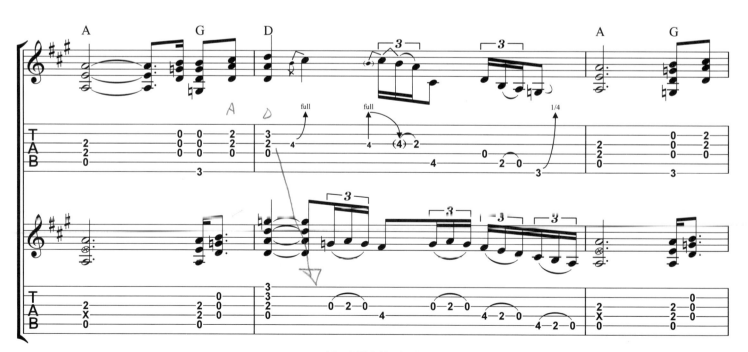

Verse

1. Girl,__ you've got those hands__ that heal,__ help me get in touch with what I feel.__
2. Girl,__ you've got those eyes__ that see,__ help me find the good that's in - side me.__

'Cos you un - der - stand__ and you sym - pa - thize,
'Cos you're the only one who rea - lly knows

18

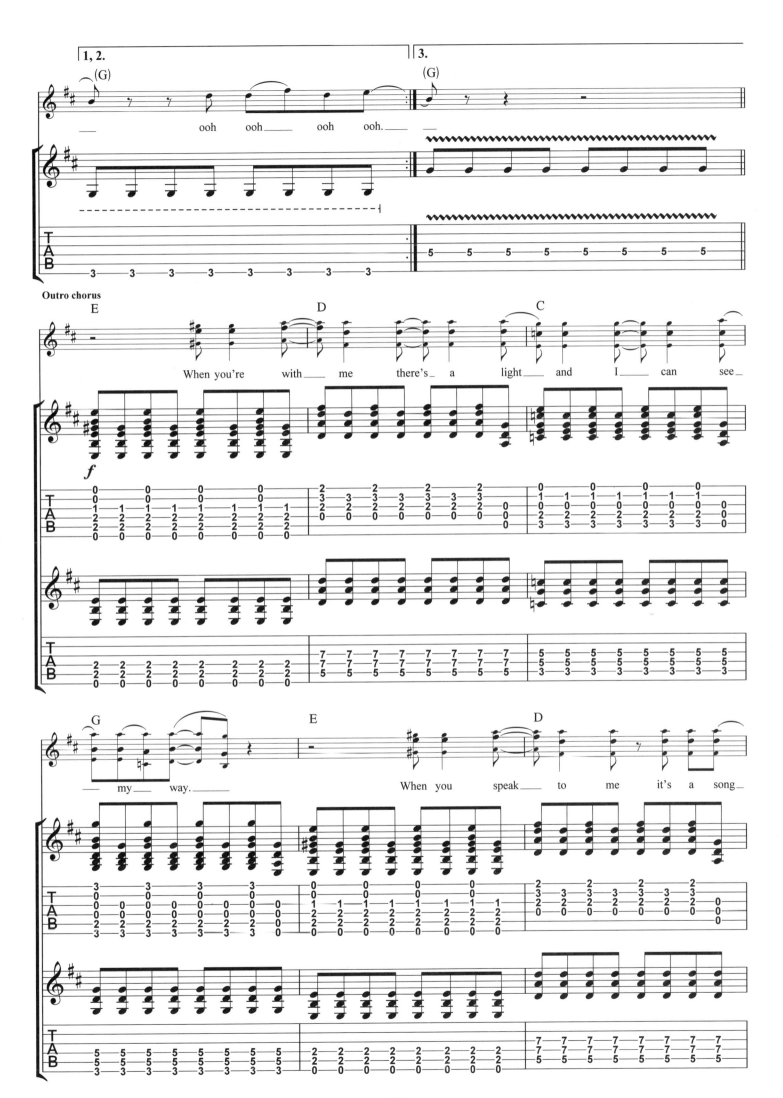

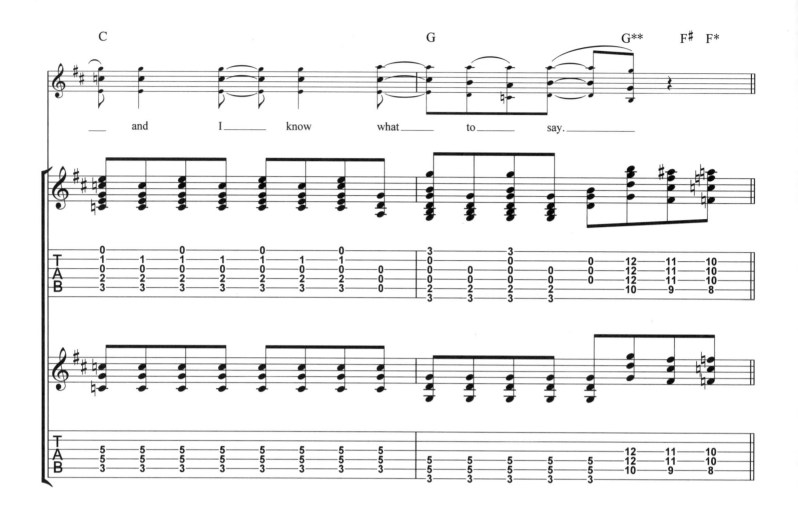

and I know what to say.

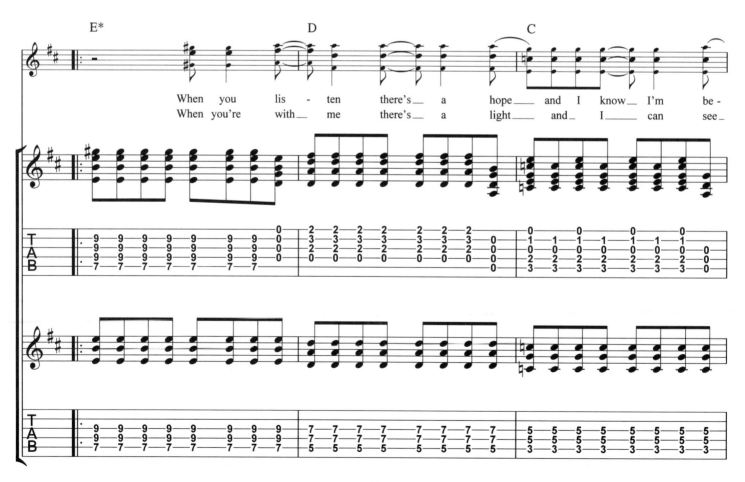

When you lis - ten there's a hope and I know I'm be -
When you're with me there's a light and I can see

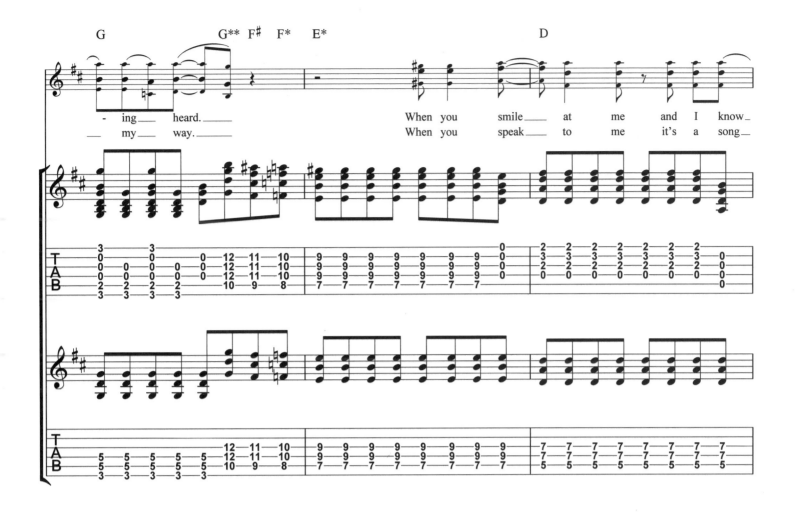

-ing___ heard.___
___ my___ way.___

When you smile___ at me and I know___
When you speak___ to me it's a song___

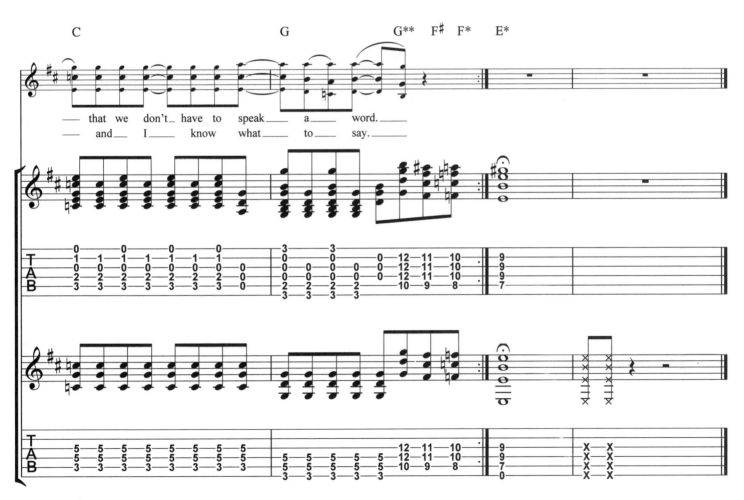

___ that we don't___ have to speak___ a___ word.___
___ and___ I___ know what___ to___ say.___

BROKEN BOY SOLDIER

WORDS & MUSIC BY
JACK WHITE & BRENDAN BENSON

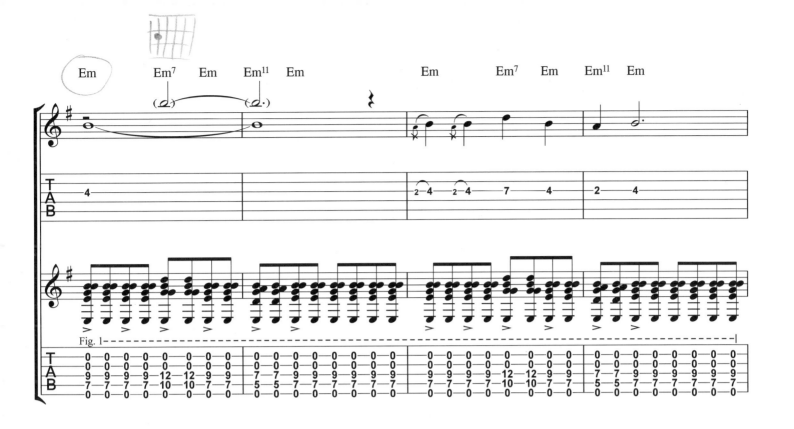

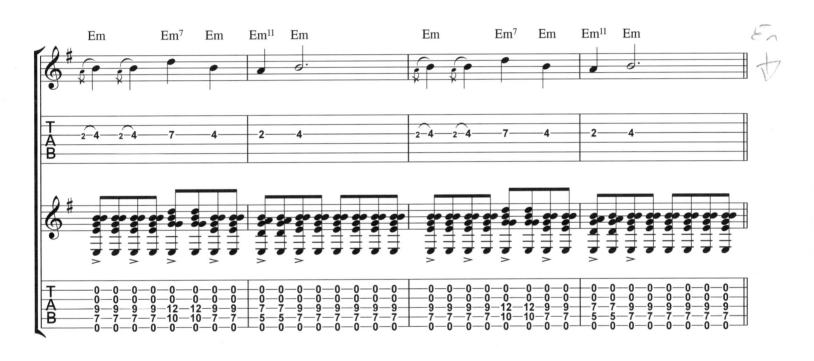

Verse

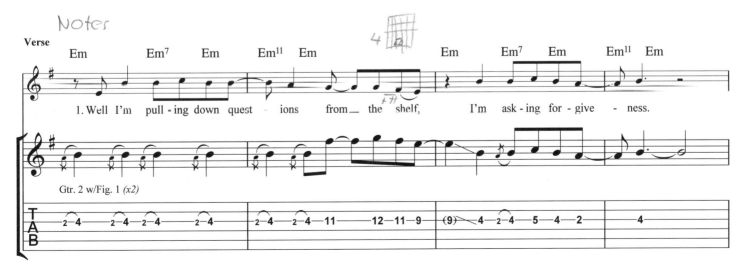

1. Well I'm pull-ing down quest-ions from the shelf, I'm ask-ing for-give - ness.

Gtr. 2 w/Fig. 1 *(x2)*

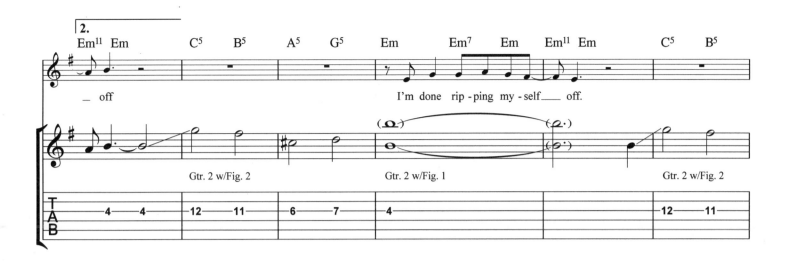

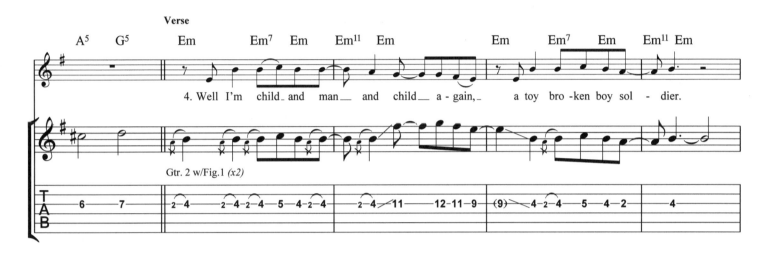

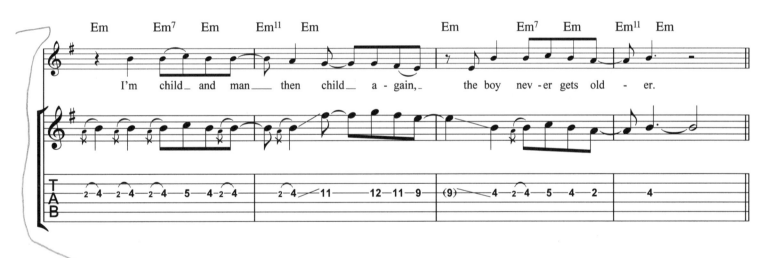

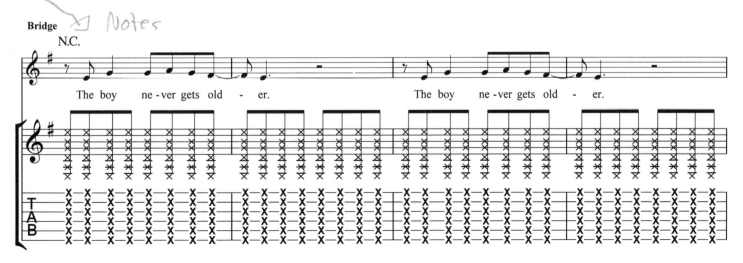

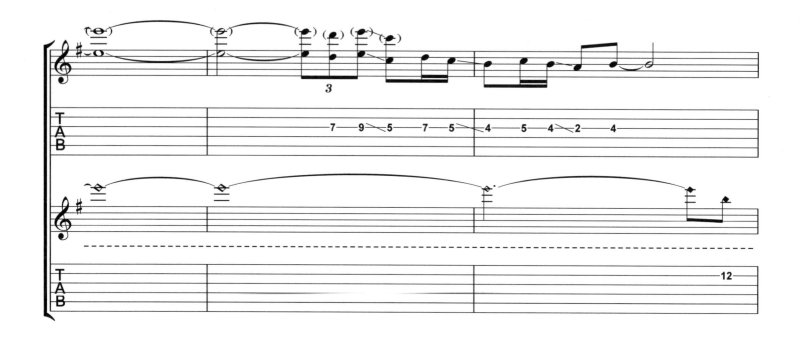

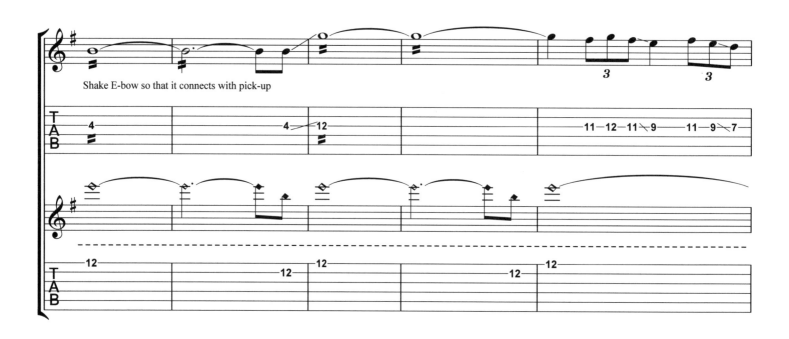

Shake E-bow so that it connects with pick-up

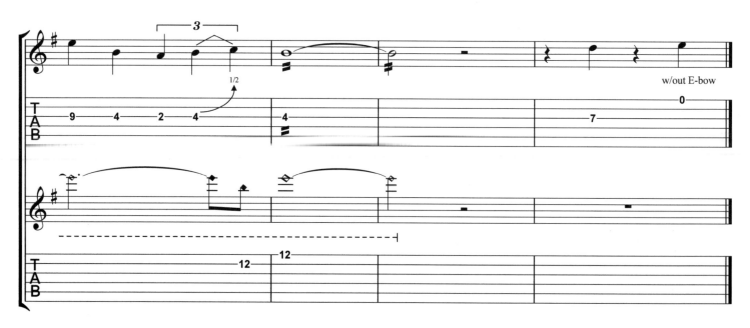

w/out E-bow

INTIMATE SECRETARY

WORDS & MUSIC BY
JACK WHITE & BRENDAN BENSON

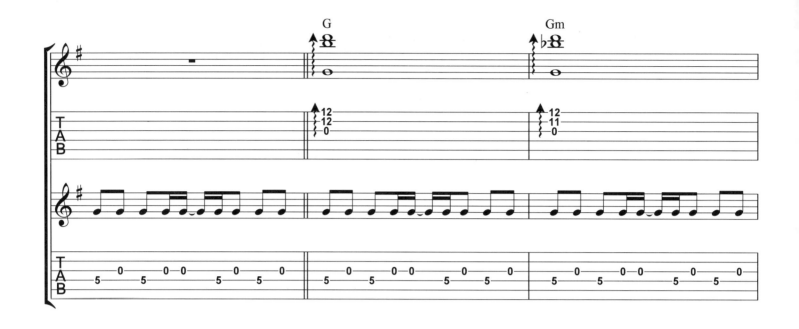

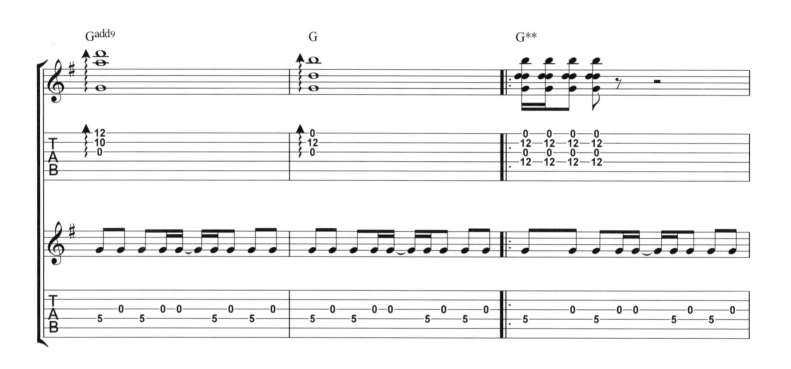

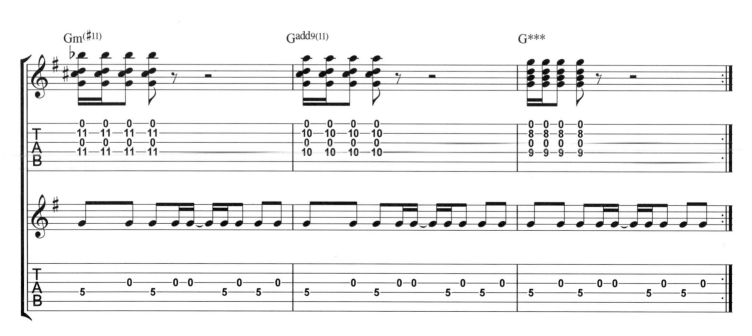

32

Vocal fig.1...
This ring-ing in my ears___ won't_ stop,___ I've got a red Ja - pa - nese_

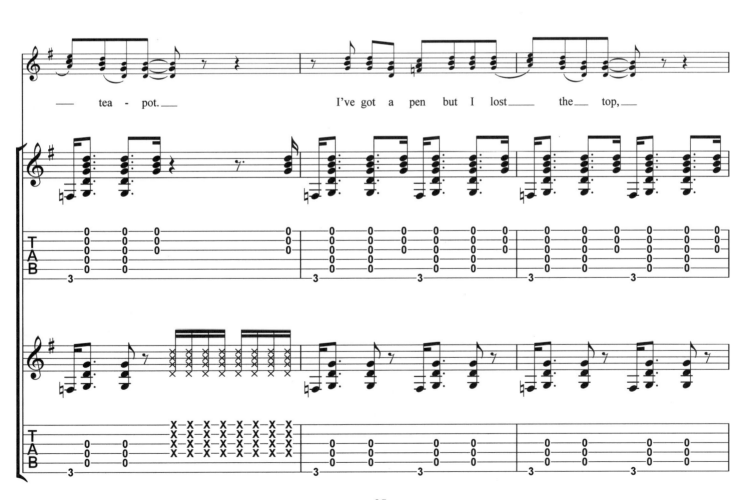

___ tea - pot.___ I've got a pen but I lost___ the__ top,___

I've got so ma - ny things you_____ have - n't got._____

...End vocal fig.1

Interlude

N.C.(G)

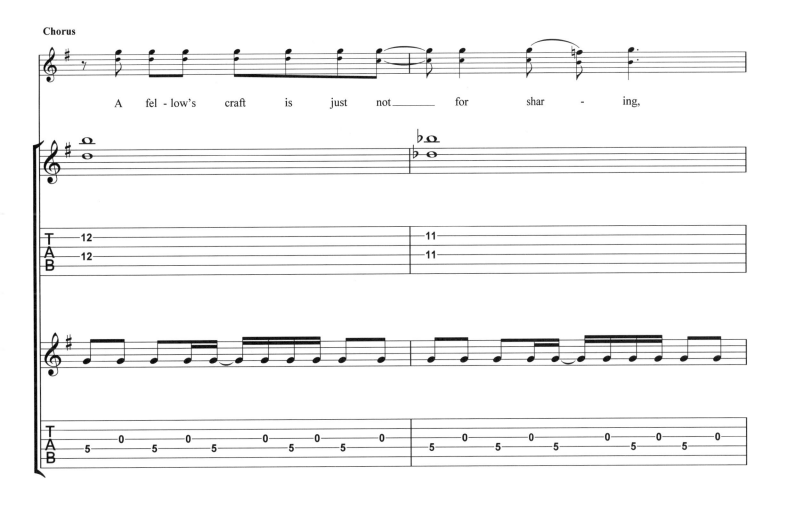

A fel-low's craft is just not_____ for shar - ing,

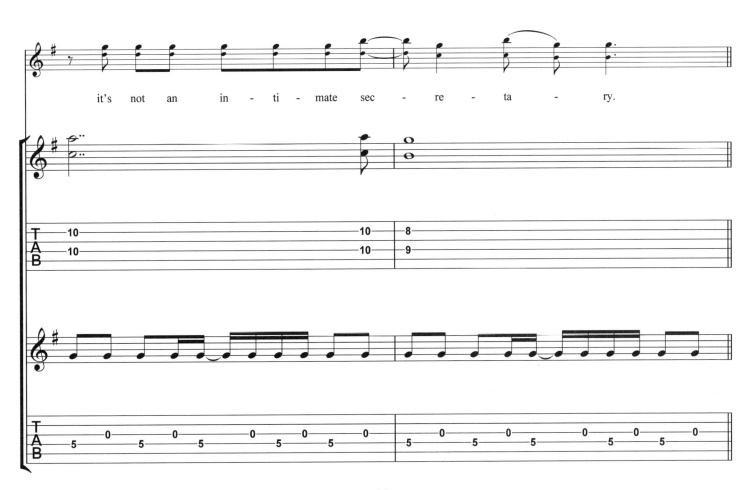

it's not an in - ti - mate sec - re - ta - ry.

I've got a rab-bit it likes___ to___ hop,___   I've got a girl and she likes___

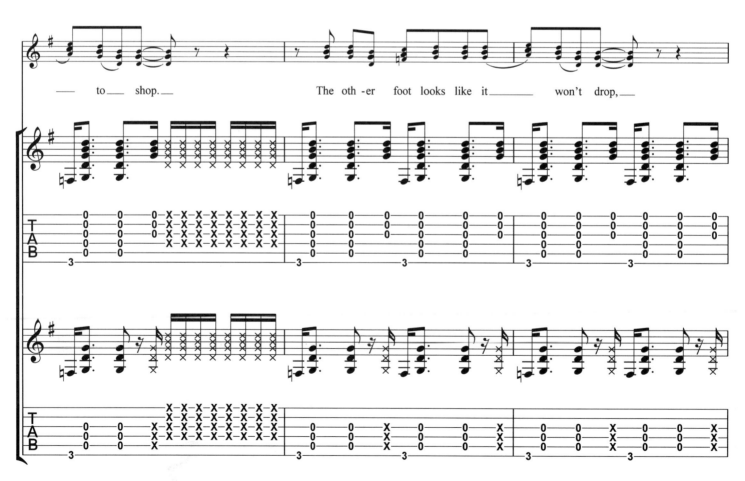

___ to___ shop.___   The oth-er foot looks like it_____ won't drop,___

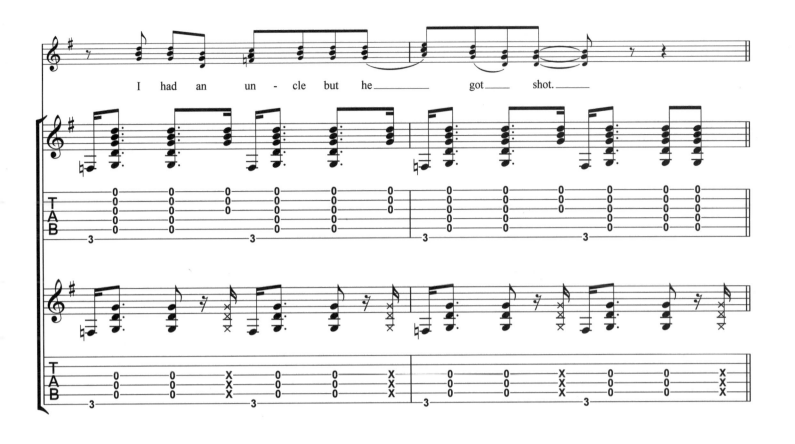

Bridge

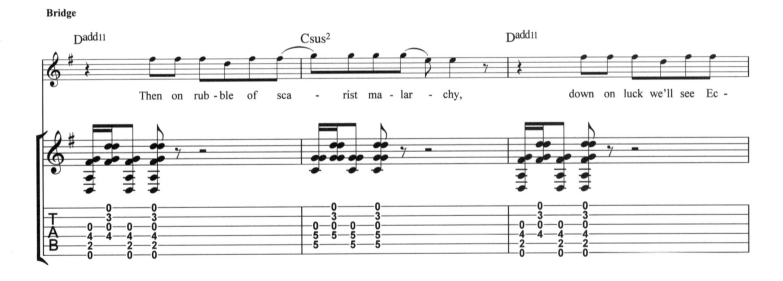

Then on rub-ble of sca - rist ma-lar - chy, down on luck we'll see Ec -

-cle - si - ar - chy. Our fel-low's craft is just not___ for sha - ring,

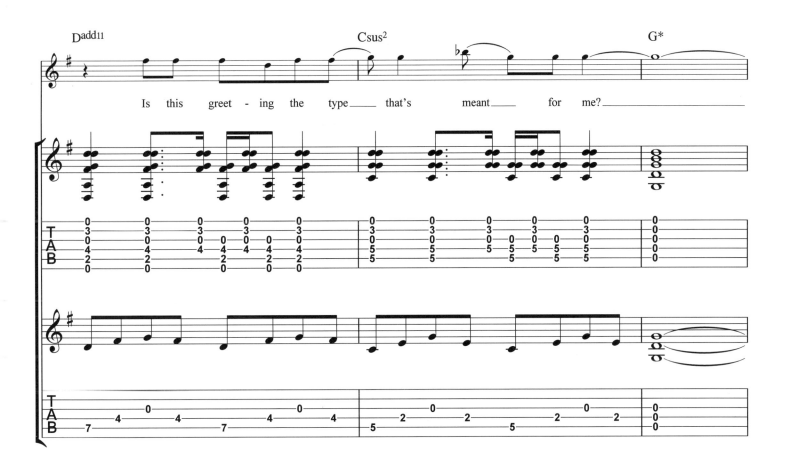

Is this greet - ing the type_____ that's_____ meant_____ for me?_____

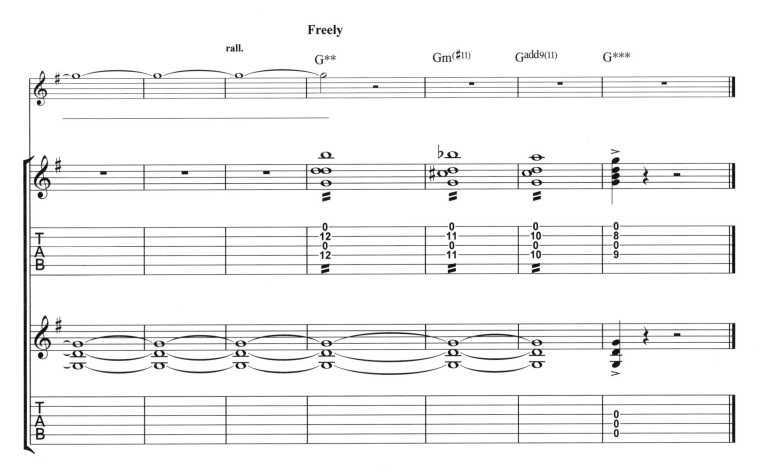

Freely

rall.

TOGETHER

WORDS & MUSIC BY
JACK WHITE & BRENDAN BENSON

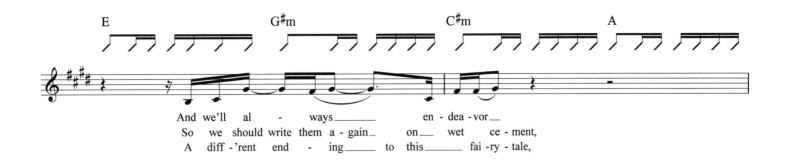

And we'll al - ways_____ en - dea - vor_____
So we should write them a - gain__ on__ wet ce - ment,
A diff -'rent end - ing_____ to this__ fai -ry - tale,

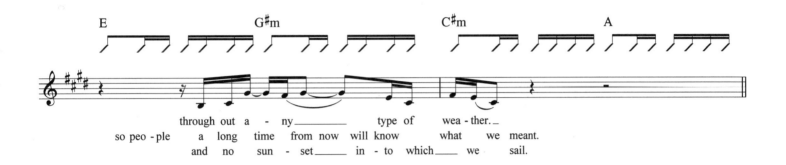

through out a - ny_____ type of wea - ther.__
so peo -ple a long time from now will know what we meant.
and no sun - set_____ in - to which__ we sail.

Chorus

You want ev -'ry - thing_____ to be__ just like, (you want ev -'ry - thing to be_
And you want ev -'ry morn - ing__ to be__ just like, (you want ev -'ry morn - ing to be_
You want ev -'ry - thing_____ to be__ just like, (you want ev -'ry - thing to be_

___ just like)__ the sto -ries that you read,____ but ne - ver write, (the sto -ries that you read, but
___ just like)__ the sto -ries that you read,____ but ne - ver write, (the sto -ries that you read, but
___ just like)__ the sto -ries that you read,____ but you__ can't write, (you__ can't__ write.)

ne -ver write.) You've got -ta learn to live   and live___ and   learn,___   mmm._____
ne -ver write.) You've got -ta learn to live   and live___ and   learn,___   oh._____
          You've got -ta learn to live   and live___ and   learn,___   oh._____

___ You've got -ta learn to give   and wait_ your turn_   or you'll get   burned._____
___ You've got -ta learn to give   and wait_ your turn,_   I'm on -ly con - cerned._____
___ You've got -ta learn to give   and wait_ your turn_   or you'll get   burned._____

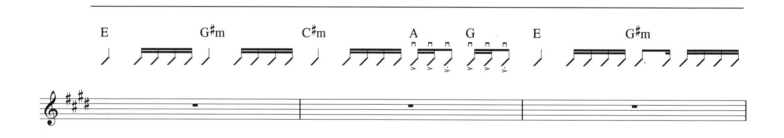

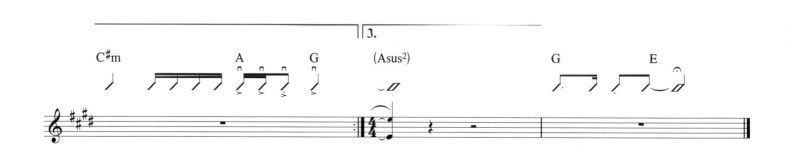

LEVEL

WORDS & MUSIC BY
JACK WHITE & BRENDAN BENSON

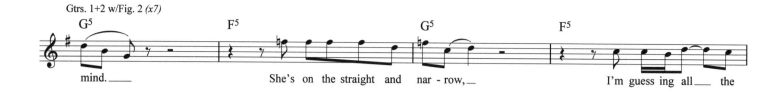

Gtrs. 1+2 w/Fig. 2 *(x7)*

mind.____ She's on the straight and nar-row,__ I'm guess ing all__ the

Gtr. 1 w/Fig. 1 *(x4)*

time.__ But I can't see the road____ if I'm look ing at__ the

signs._____ I'm car-ry-ing a load__ and step-pingout__ of

Interlude

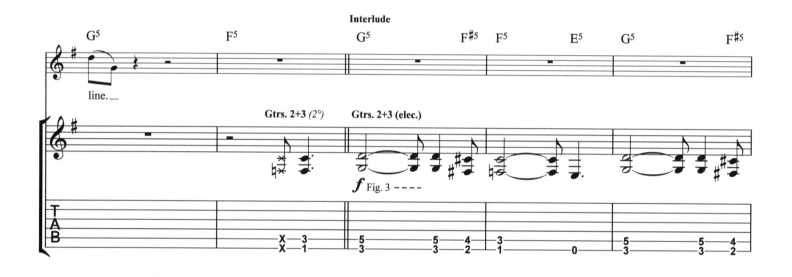

line.__

Gtrs. 2+3 *(2°)* Gtrs. 2+3 (elec.)

f Fig. 3 - - - -

To Coda ⊕

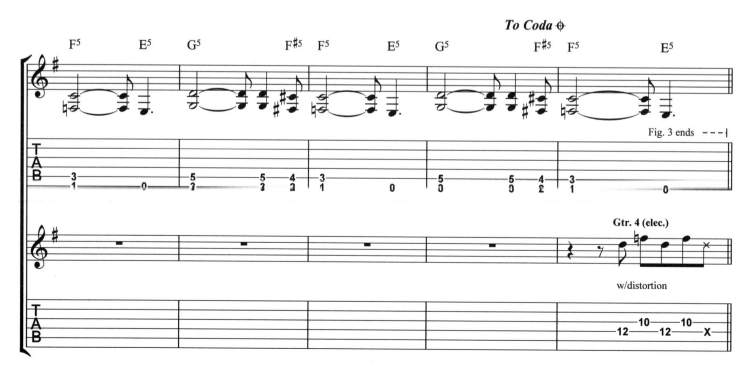

Fig. 3 ends - - - ╎

Gtr. 4 (elec.)

w/distortion

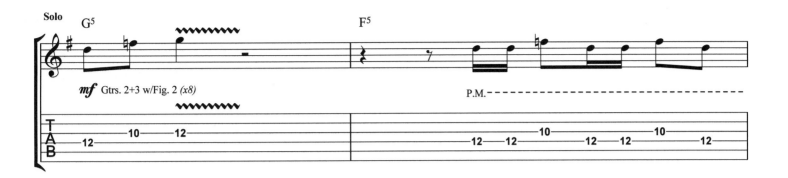

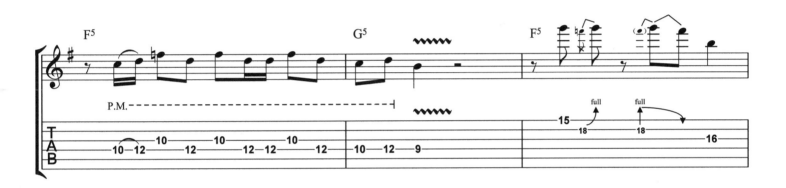

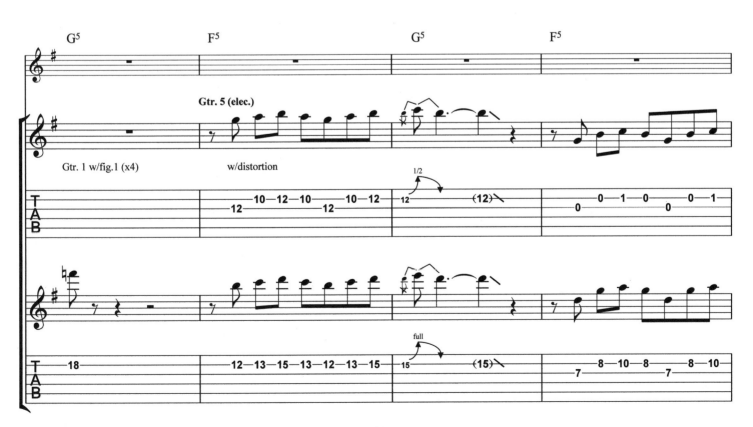

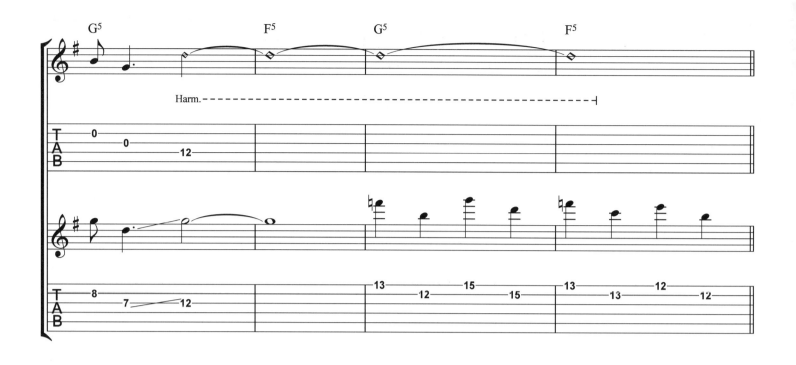

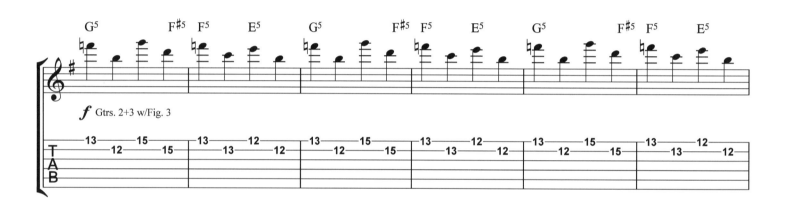

D.S. al Coda

Coda

My ba-by's on the

Gtrs. 2+3

STORE BOUGHT BONES

WORDS & MUSIC BY
JACK WHITE & BRENDAN BENSON

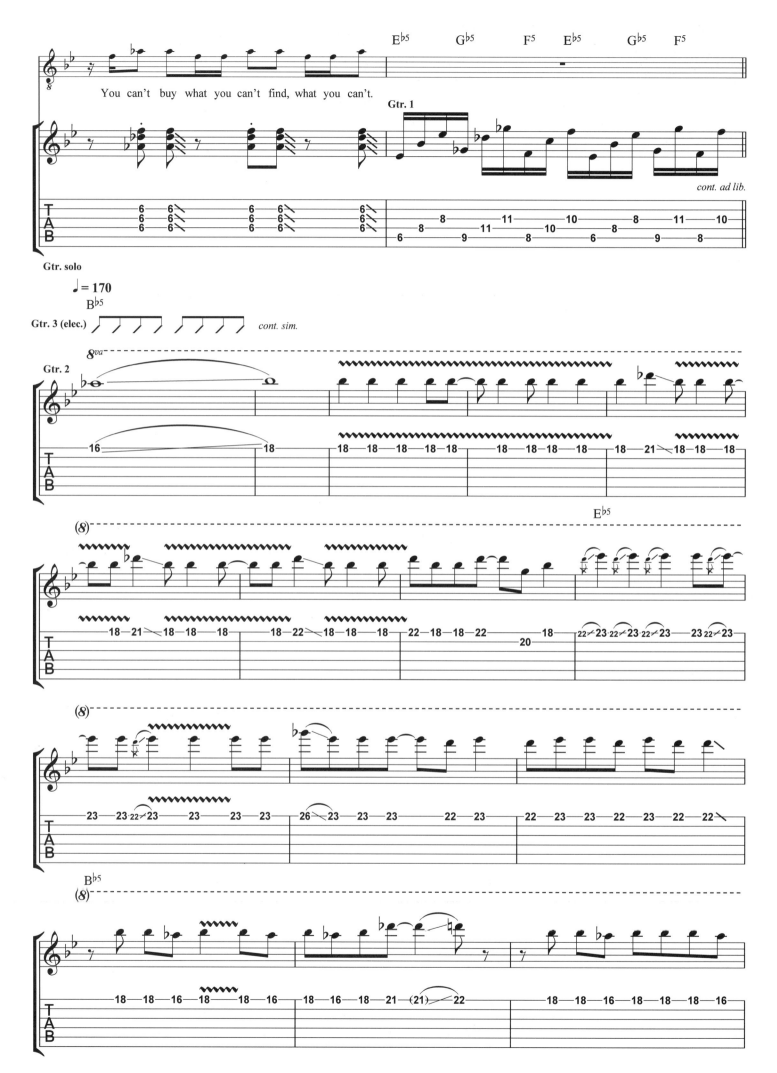

You can't buy what you can't find, what you can't.

YELLOW SUN

WORDS & MUSIC BY
JACK WHITE & BRENDAN BENSON

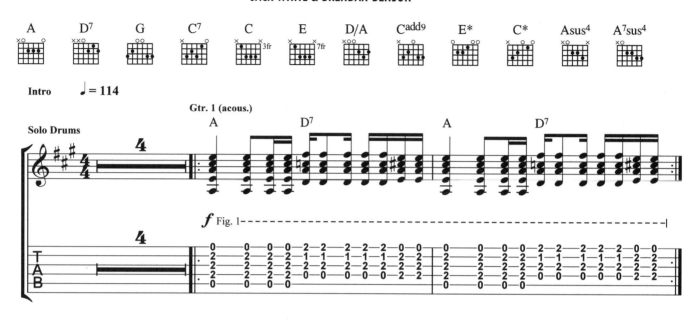

Intro ♩ = 114

Solo Drums

Gtr. 1 (acous.)

ff Fig. 1

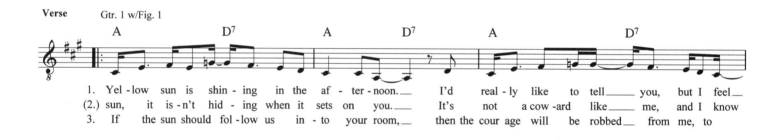

Verse   Gtr. 1 w/Fig. 1

1. Yel-low sun is shin-ing in the af-ter-noon.___ I'd real-ly like to tell___ you, but I feel___
(2.) sun, it is-n't hid-ing when it sets on you.___ It's not a cow-ard like___ me, and I know
3. If the sun should fol-low us in-to your room,___ then the cour-age will be robbed___ from me, to

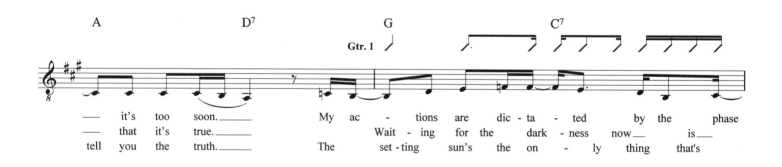

Gtr. 1

___ it's too soon._____ My ac - tions are dic - ta - ted by the phase
___ that it's true._____ Wait - ing for the dark - ness now___ is___
tell you the truth._____ The set - ting sun's the on - ly thing that's

Gtr. 1 w/Fig. 1

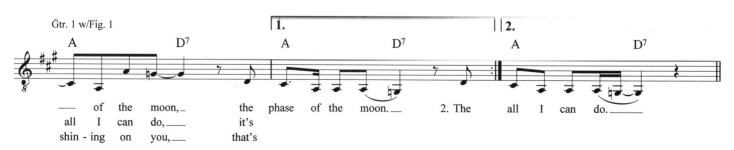

1.   2.

___ of the moon,___ the phase of the moon.   2. The   all I can do.___
all I can do,___ it's
shin - ing on you,___ that's

55

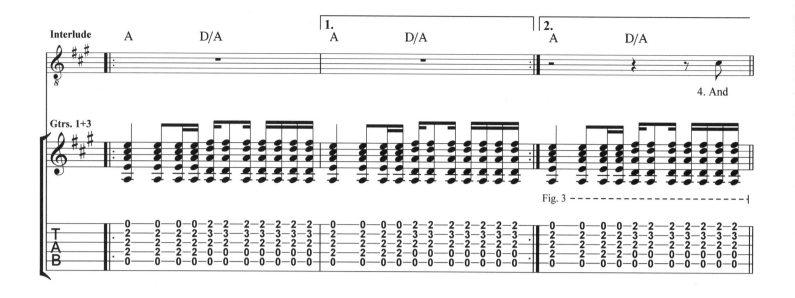

Interlude

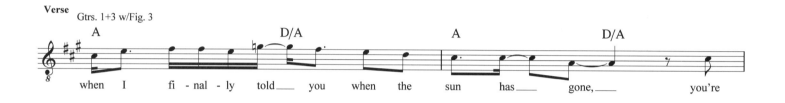

Verse Gtrs. 1+3 w/Fig. 3

when I fi- nal- ly told___ you when the sun has___ gone,___ you're

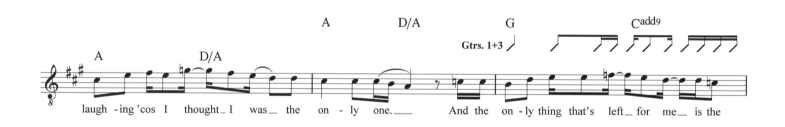

laugh- ing 'cos I thought_ I was_ the on- ly one.___ And the on- ly thing that's left_ for me _ is the

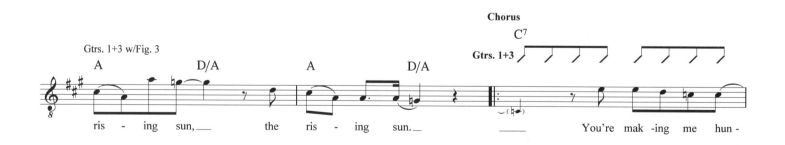

Gtrs. 1+3 w/Fig. 3

ris- ing sun,___ the ris- ing sun.___ ___ You're mak- ing me hun-

- gry,_____ you're mak- ing me hun- gry._____ but what's real- ly fun-

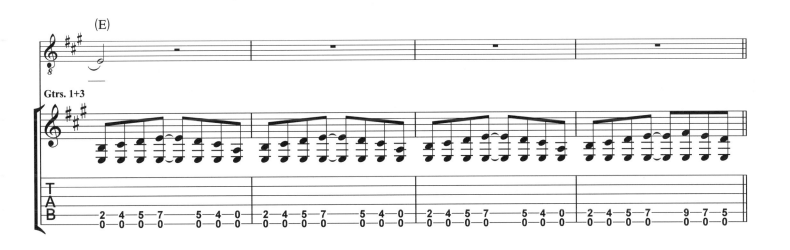

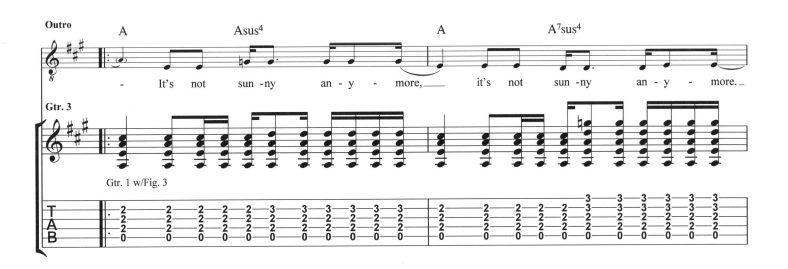

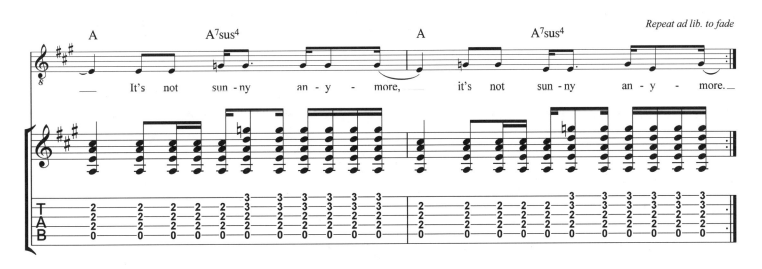

CALL IT A DAY

WORDS & MUSIC BY
JACK WHITE & BRENDAN BENSON

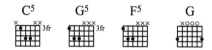

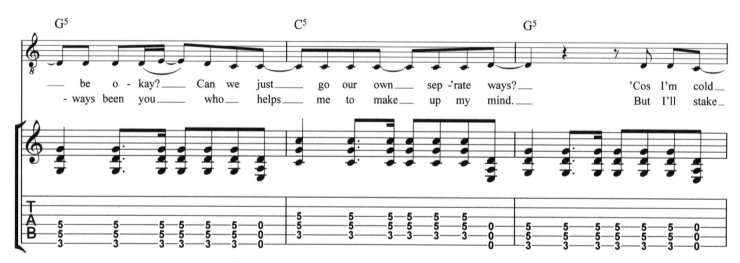

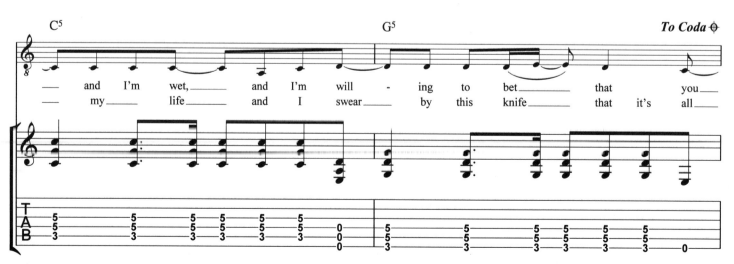

BLUE VEINS

WORDS & MUSIC BY
JACK WHITE & BRENDAN BENSON

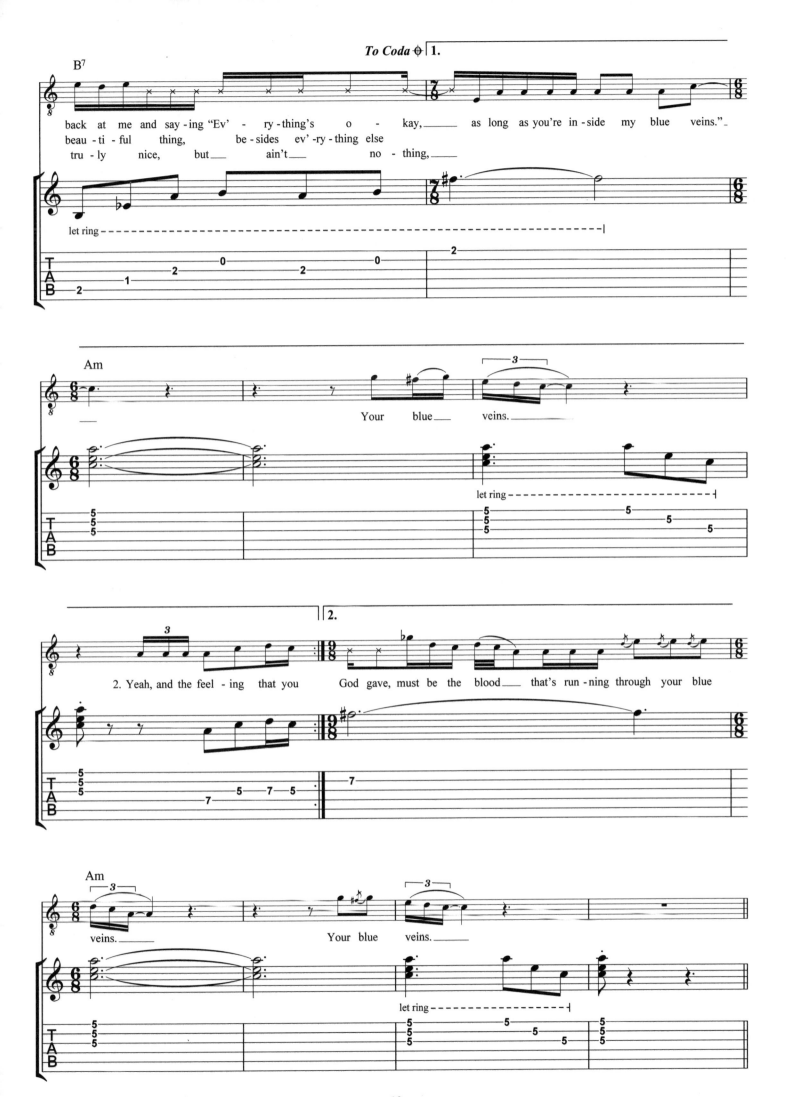

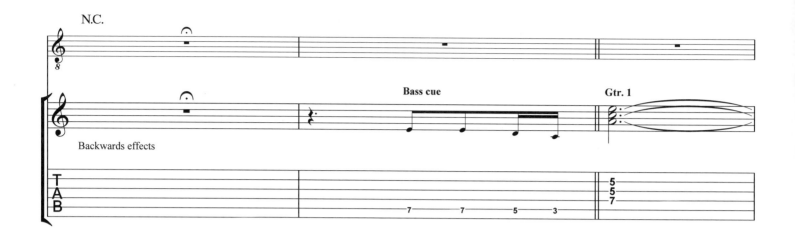

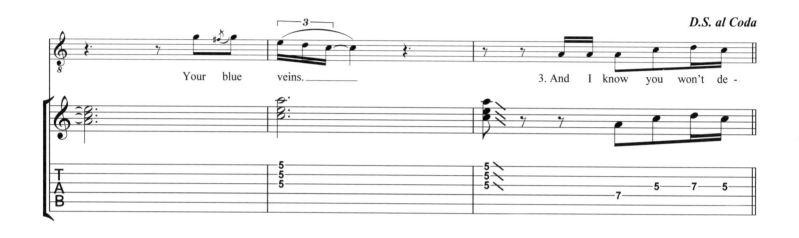

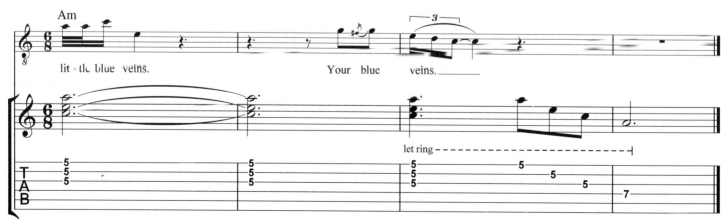